little book of
menus

contents

menus to make
your mouth water

With so much fab Free Food to choose from when you're Food Optimising, deciding what to have for each breakfast, lunch and dinner can be a challenge (a nice challenge!). So in this essential little book we've done the planning for you and created 60 magnificent menus that will make everyday eating even easier than ever!

You'll find 60 brilliant breakfasts including toffee apple porridge and bacon frittata, 60 luscious lunches like coronation chicken pasta and hot dog jackets, and 60 dinners to die for such as Tex-Mex steak salad and spiced salmon with mango couscous.

There are handy chapters for the times when you're watching the pennies and the occasions when you want to push the boat out, for the days when the sun is shining and the days when the cold leaves you craving comfort, not forgetting those moments when you can't get a food fix fast enough!

Every menu is satisfying, full of flavour and beautifully balanced and, best of all, every one of these 180 recipes is completely Free. Some of the days feature your essential Healthy Extras to make meals even more delicious (see page 8)!

meals to make your day – every day!

your guide to using our
little book of menus

With this essential little book in your kitchen, Food Optimising is about to become easier than ever! Before you dive in, here are a few tips for getting the most out of your new cookbook.

- Every recipe in this book is **completely Free (with some including your Healthy Extra 'a' and/or 'b' choices)**. We've carefully selected the menus to give a great balance of meat, poultry and fish, a wide variety of fruit and veg, plus satisfying staples like pasta, potatoes and rice. So if you want to keep things really simple, just pick a day you're in the mood for and enjoy!

- If you want to **pick and mix your meals** to fit your food preferences, feel free to choose breakfast, lunch and dinner from different menus within the book. If you do pick and mix, make sure you have one Healthy Extra 'a' and one Healthy Extra 'b' – as well as your choice of Syns.

- For your very best weight losses, **fill one-third of your plate with Speed food** at every mealtime. Most vegetables are Speed food and can be fresh, frozen or canned. A lot of fresh or frozen fruits are Speed food too (with a few exceptions like avocado and dates, which have Syns), so eat them as much as you like. Health experts also recommend we eat at least five portions of fruit and vegetables a day, so we say have at least that much – or more if you like!

- We've marked any recipes that could be suitable for an Extra Easy *SP* day – just make sure you follow the *SP* guidelines in your Food Optimising book when you put your menu together.

- If you find yourself needing a little something to keep you going between meals, **Speed fruit and veg are the perfect choice**. You could also choose snacks from the Healthy Extras list if you're not having them as part of your menu (see our selection on page 8) or from your daily Syns allowance (see page 142).

- To stay hydrated and for good digestion, aim to **drink at least eight glasses a day** – and vary your drinks to include water or low-calorie drinks as well as tea or coffee (sorry, alcohol doesn't count!).

For more handy hints on successful Food Optimising, see our cook's tips on page 140.

sticky beef noodles, page 30

Healthy Extras®

As well as all that Free Food, you can enjoy your Healthy Extra 'a' and Healthy Extra 'b' choices every day. Healthy Extra 'a' choices are high in calcium, while Healthy Extra 'b' choices are high in fibre or contain important nutrients for a balanced diet.

Some of the menus in this book include a Healthy Extra 'a' and many contain a Healthy Extra 'b' as part of breakfast or lunch. Feel free to swap them with other options on these lists, and if your chosen menu doesn't use one or other of them, have them as healthy snacks, starters or desserts instead.

Selected Healthy Extra 'a' choices

Milk

- 350ml skimmed milk
- 250ml semi-skimmed milk
- 175ml whole milk
- 1 litre unsweetened calcium-enriched plain almond drink
- 400ml unsweetened calcium-enriched plain soya drink
- 250ml calcium-enriched plain rice drink

Cheese

- 30g Cheddar or Lactofree Mature Cheddar
- 40g reduced-fat Cheddar
- 45g feta
- 65g reduced-fat feta/Greek-style salad cheese
- 35g halloumi
- 50g mozzarella (cows' milk)
- 30g Parmesan/Parmigiano-Reggiano/Grana Padano, fresh
- 90g ricotta
- 75g reduced-fat/light soft cheese (plain)
- 3 Dairylea Original Triangles
- 4 Dairylea Light Triangles
- 6 The Laughing Cow Extra Light Triangles
- 2 Mini Babybel Original Cheeses
- 3 Mini Babybel Light Cheeses

Selected Healthy Extra 'b' choices

Bread & crispbreads

- 60g of any wholemeal bread
- 60g wholemeal roll
- 2 medium slices wholemeal bread (400g sliced loaf)
- 2 medium slices gluten-free wholemeal/multigrain bread
- 1 slice wholemeal bread (800g sliced loaf)
- 50g rye bread
- 6 Finn Crisp Original Rye/Multigrain Thin Crispbreads
- 5 Real Foods Original/Sesame Corn Thins
- 4 Ryvita Dark Rye/Original Crispbreads
- 3 Ryvita Deli Multigrain/Pumpkin Seeds & Oats/Sesame/Sunflower Seeds & Oats/Sweet Onion Crispbreads

Dried, canned & cooked fruit

- 65g dried prunes
- 60g dried apricots
- 50g dried figs
- 350g canned pears, in juice
- 125g canned breakfast apricots, in juice
- 500g cooked rhubarb
- 400g cooked plums
- 300g cooked blackberries
- 250g cooked eating apples
- 250g cooked raspberries

Cereals & cereal bars

- 50g high-fibre wheat bran cereal eg. Kellogg's All-Bran Original
- 45g bran flakes
- 45g Dorset Cereals Simply Delicious Muesli
- 45g fruit-filled wheat biscuits, blueberry/raisin
- 45g Jordans Natural No Added Sugar Muesli
- 40g Alpen No Added Sugar Muesli
- 40g bite-size wheats, plain
- 40g Dorset Cereals Simply Nutty Muesli
- 40g Kellogg's All-Bran Golden Crunch
- 40g malt wheats cereal, plain, eg. Nestlé Shreddies
- 40g puffed wheat
- 40g Post Grape-Nuts
- 40g plain porridge oats
- 2 Hi-fi bars
- 2 Nestlé Shredded Wheat
- 2 wholewheat biscuits eg. Weetabix

Nuts & seeds

- 16 almonds
- 5 brazil nuts
- 14 cashew nuts
- 23 hazelnuts
- 30 peanuts, plain
- 11 pecan halves
- 35 pistachio nuts
- 2 level tbsp pumpkin/sesame/sunflower seeds
- 5 walnut halves

Healthy Extras

fast & Free®

Satisfaction is guaranteed with these quick menus – perfect for those days when you can't get food on the table fast enough.

birds and the beans

breakfast

banoffee tower

serves 1 / ready in 5 minutes

Layer sliced banana and Müllerlight Toffee yogurt in a glass. Top with a dollop of plain quark and more banana.

lunch

garden frittata Ⓥ

serves 1 / ready in 15 minutes

Fry chopped red onions with halved cherry tomatoes in low-calorie cooking spray until softened. Add drained canned sweetcorn and peas and pour in a few beaten eggs. Season and cook until set, finishing under the grill.

dinner

chicken and cannellini bean casserole ❄ SP

serves 4 / ready in 25 minutes

Spray a large frying pan with low-calorie cooking spray and place over a high heat. Cut 4 skinless and boneless chicken breasts into large chunks and fry for 5 minutes, turning to brown all over. Add 2 halved and sliced courgettes and fry for 2 minutes, then add ½ tsp fennel seeds, 2 x 400g cans cherry tomatoes plus their juices and a drained 400g can cannellini beans. Season and bring to the boil, then cover and simmer for 10 minutes or until the chicken is cooked. Stir in 150g baby spinach and wilt for a few minutes then serve hot. Follow with a bowl of fresh cherries.

mint condition

breakfast

turkey bacon and eggs

serves 1 / ready in 10 minutes

Fry lean turkey bacon rashers, visible fat
removed, and eggs in low-calorie cooking
spray and serve with baked beans. Follow
with a ripe pear.

lunch

tuna melt

serves 1 / ready in 10 minutes

Drain tuna chunks in spring water and mix with chopped red
onion, sliced radishes and fat-free natural fromage frais. Pile it
on to 2 medium slices of wholemeal toast from a small 400g loaf
(Healthy Extra 'b'), top with 70g reduced-fat mozzarella chunks
(Healthy Extra 'a') and grill until bubbling.

dinner

herbed pork with minted couscous

serves 4 / ready in 25 minutes

Put 300g plain dried couscous in a heatproof bowl and add 1 finely chopped carrot, 1 chopped roasted red pepper in brine from a jar, 4 chopped tomatoes and 6 sliced spring onions. Pour over 375ml boiling vegetable stock, cover with cling film and stand for 15 minutes. Meanwhile, mix the zest and juice of 1 lemon and 1 tsp each onion granules, ground coriander and dried mixed herbs, rub the mixture all over 4 large or 8 small pork steaks, visible fat removed, and season. Cook the pork on a hot griddle pan for 2 minutes each side then roast at 200°C/fan 180°C/gas 6 for 5 minutes or until cooked. Roughly chop 50g baby spinach leaves and ½ small pack fresh mint, fork it through the couscous and top with the pork to serve.

living on the kedge

breakfast
peach melba crunch
serves 1 / ready in 5 minutes

Layer a Müllerlight Vanilla yogurt with 40g All Bran Golden Crunch (Healthy Extra 'b'), raspberries and sliced fresh peach.

lunch
meaty ploughman's *SP*
serves 1 / ready in 5 minutes

Pile up a plate with 3 Mini Babybel Light cheeses (Healthy Extra 'a'), pickled onions, cornichons, cooked beetroot, salad leaves, apple wedges and cold cuts of lean cooked beef or turkey, visible fat removed.

dinner
salmon kedgeree
serves 4 / ready in 30 minutes

Cook 300g dried basmati rice according to the pack instructions, adding 2 tbsp curry powder while it cooks. Drain well. Meanwhile, put 4 skinless salmon fillets in a wide pan, cover with boiling water and a lid and simmer for 10 minutes or until cooked. Lift out and flake the fish, discarding any fine bones, and add to the drained rice along with 8 thinly sliced spring onions and 2 tbsp each chopped fresh parsley and coriander. Season, stir to combine and top each plate with half an egg, cooked to your liking (see page 140), and coriander sprigs. Serve with lemon wedges and salad.

salad days

breakfast

tropical pot 🅥

serves 1 / ready in 5 minutes

Layer prepared fresh mango chunks in a glass with fat-free natural Greek yogurt and sliced banana. Dust with ground ginger.

lunch

houmous salad 🅥

serves 1 / ready in 15 minutes

Whizz together drained 400g can chickpeas, 2 tbsp fat-free natural yogurt, 2 tbsp lemon juice and 1 crushed garlic clove to make houmous. Dollop it over a salad of rocket, chopped red onion, grated carrot, diced cucumber and tomato, and chunks of toast made using 2 medium slices wholemeal bread from a small 400g loaf (Healthy Extra 'b').

dinner

courgetti carbonara

serves 4 / ready in 15 minutes

Cook 350g dried spaghetti according to the pack instructions, adding 300g courgetti (or 2 shredded courgettes) for the last minute. Meanwhile, spray a large frying pan with low-calorie cooking spray and place over a medium-high heat. Roughly chop 8 back bacon rashers, visible fat removed, and stir-fry for 2-3 minutes. Add 4 chopped garlic cloves and stir-fry for 30 seconds. Drain the spaghetti and courgetti, return to the pan off the heat and add the bacon. Quickly add 3 lightly beaten egg yolks and toss to coat the spaghetti and courgetti – the egg will cook a little in the heat (see page 140). Sprinkle with fresh parsley, grind over a little black pepper and serve with lots of salad. Follow with fresh strawberries topped with Danone Activia 0% Fat Strawberry yogurt.

talking turkey

breakfast

ham and egg bap *SP*

serves 1 / ready in 10 minutes

A bowl of fresh orange and grapefruit segments plus a 60g wholemeal roll (Healthy Extra 'b'), split and filled with lots of sliced tomato, an egg fried in low-calorie cooking spray and 1 slice of lean ham, visible fat removed.

lunch

supercharged stir-fry *V* **vegan**

serves 1 / ready in 15 minutes

Fry thinly sliced onion, red pepper, carrots and cabbage in low-calorie cooking spray for 5 minutes. Add cooked dried rice noodles and a splash of soy sauce and cook for a couple more minutes.

dinner

turkey steaks with chunky onion sauce

serves 4 / ready in 25 minutes

Put 1 sliced onion, 1 finely chopped garlic clove, 200g chopped mushrooms, 2 chopped tomatoes, 1 tsp dried mixed herbs and 200ml boiling chicken stock in a saucepan over a high heat. Bring to the boil and simmer for 10 minutes or until thickened. Meanwhile, cook 4 lean turkey breast steaks in a griddle or frying pan over a high heat for 3-4 minutes on each side or until cooked through. Season the sauce to taste and serve with the turkey steaks, your favourite potatoes, extra Speed veg and a sprinkling of roughly chopped fresh parsley.

fast & Free 21

from rasher with love

breakfast

classic BLT SP

serves 1 / ready in 10 minutes

Grill 2 back bacon rashers, visible fat removed, and sandwich between 2 medium slices of wholemeal toast from a small 400g loaf (Healthy Extra 'b'), along with crisp lettuce and sliced tomato. Follow with fresh apricots.

lunch

chicken and egg salad

serves 1 / ready in 15 minutes

Fill a lunchbox with salad leaves, cooked and sliced skinless chicken breast, cooked mangetout, sliced cucumber and a halved boiled egg or 2, cooked to your liking (see page 140). Drizzle with balsamic vinegar or fat-free vinaigrette.

dinner

bean feast ❄ Ⓥ vegan

serves 4 / ready in 30 minutes

Spray a large frying pan with low-calorie cooking spray and place over a low heat. Roughly chop 2 medium onions, 2 carrots and 2 celery sticks, add to the pan and cook for 10 minutes, stirring occasionally. Add 2 chopped garlic cloves, 1 tbsp tomato purée and ¼ tsp fennel seeds and fry for 1-2 minutes. Add 400g can chopped tomatoes then fill the can with water and add that too. Season and simmer for 10 minutes then add 3 drained 400g cans of beans or pulses in water (your choice), 200g shredded kale and a splash more water, if needed. Cook for a few more minutes to wilt the kale then scatter with parsley to serve.

squid's in

breakfast

sweet wheats Ⓥ ⓈⓅ

serves 1 / ready in 5 minutes

Pour milk from your daily
Healthy Extra 'a' allowance
over 40g puffed wheat (Healthy
Extra 'b') and top with fresh
raspberries.

lunch

spicy beef couscous

serves 2 / ready in 20 minutes

Soak 100g dried couscous in boiling water for
10 minutes. Meanwhile, fry 250g lean beef mince
(5% fat or less), 200g frozen mixed vegetables
and 1 tsp each ground cumin and curry powder
for 8-10 minutes. Drain off any fat and stir it all
through the couscous with some chopped fresh
coriander. Follow with fresh plums.

dinner

garlic squid and prawn tagliatelle

serves 4 / ready in 20 minutes

Cook 400g dried tagliatelle according to the pack instructions. Meanwhile, spray a large
frying pan with low-calorie cooking spray and place over a high heat. Add 300g prepared
squid rings and cook for 2 minutes or until golden. Lift out and set aside. Add 3 finely
chopped garlic cloves and 6 sliced spring onions to the pan and stir-fry for 2 minutes,
then add 300g halved baby plum tomatoes and 225g raw peeled prawns. Cook for
a further 2-3 minutes or until the prawns are pink then return the squid to the pan
and toss lightly. Drain the pasta, reserving a little of the cooking water, and stir in
50g rocket, the seafood mixture and a splash of the cooking water. Season and
add the juice of ½ lemon to serve.

keep it sweet

breakfast

cheese and mushroom omelette Ⓥ 🅢🅟

serves 1 / ready in 10 minutes

Fry chopped mushrooms in low-calorie cooking spray, pour in beaten eggs and cook until set. Top with 40g reduced-fat Cheddar (Healthy Extra 'a') and grill until melted. Serve with some grilled cherry tomatoes.

lunch

smoked salmon pasta

serves 1 / ready in 15 minutes

Peel a small cucumber into ribbons with a vegetable peeler and dry-fry briefly. Stir into cooked and cooled dried pasta along with smoked salmon trimmings, cooked cauliflower or broccoli florets, chopped fresh dill and lemon juice.

dinner

sweet potato curry ❄ Ⓥ vegan (without the yogurt)

serves 4 / ready in 30 minutes

Put 1 chopped onion, 3 chopped garlic cloves, 2cm piece root ginger, peeled and grated, 1 tbsp curry powder and 400g passata in a large saucepan. Pour in 450ml boiling vegetable stock and bring to the boil. Reduce the heat to medium-low, simmer for 7-8 minutes and season to taste. Peel 2 large potatoes and 2 large sweet potatoes and cut into chunks along with 3 red peppers. Add to the pan and simmer for 15 minutes or until tender, then scatter with fresh coriander sprigs and serve with paprika-spiced yogurt. Follow with fresh mango slices.

the french connection

breakfast

wake-up crumble 🕖

serves 1 / ready in 5 minutes

Layer fresh blackberries in a glass
with fat-free natural fromage frais
or yogurt and crumble over your
favourite Hi-fi bar (½ x Healthy
Extra 'b').

lunch

power pasta 🕖 vegan

serves 1 / ready in 15 minutes

Cook and cool dried pasta and mix
with drained canned flageolet beans,
chopped tomatoes, cooked sugar
snap peas and red onion. Drizzle with
fat-free vinaigrette and lemon juice
and scatter with basil leaves. Follow
with grapes.

dinner

quick chicken chasseur ❄

serves 4 / ready in 30 minutes

Spray a frying pan with low-calorie cooking
spray and place over a medium heat. Cut
8 back bacon rashers, visible fat removed,
into large chunks and stir-fry for 2 minutes
or until starting to brown. Cut 4 skinless
and boneless chicken breasts into large
chunks, add to the pan and stir-fry for
3-4 minutes. Increase the heat to high
and add 200g baby button mushrooms,
2 chopped shallots, 2 chopped garlic
cloves, 2 chopped tomatoes and
300ml boiling chicken stock. Bring to
the boil and simmer for 12-15 minutes or
until thickened and bubbling, stirring often.
Season, add a splash of Worcestershire
sauce and scatter over 2 tbsp chopped
fresh parsley. Serve with mashed potatoes
and extra Speed vegetables. Follow with a
Hi-fi bar (½ x Healthy Extra 'b').

stir crazy

breakfast

muesli with figs ⓥ

serves 1 / ready in 5 minutes

Top 40g Dorset Cereals Simply
Nutty Muesli (Healthy Extra 'b')
with fat-free natural Greek yogurt
and sliced fresh figs and apple.

lunch

speedy tuna niçoise

serves 1 / ready in 10 minutes

Toss salad leaves with cherry
tomatoes, quartered hard-boiled egg,
diced cucumber, drained canned baby
potatoes in water and drained canned
tuna in spring water. Drizzle with fat-free
vinaigrette. Follow with a ripe pear.

dinner

sticky beef noodles

serves 4 / ready in 20 minutes

Boil 250g dried noodles according to the pack instructions then drain and set
aside. Meanwhile, spray a large frying pan with low-calorie cooking spray and place
over a high heat. Stir-fry 450g sliced lean steak, visible fat removed, 2 chopped
garlic cloves and 1 deseeded and chopped red chilli for 2 minutes. Transfer to
a plate then wipe the pan, spray again and stir-fry 2 carrots, peeled and cut into
matchsticks, for 2 minutes. Add 200g thickly sliced pak choi and 250g rinsed fresh
bean sprouts and cook for 3 minutes. Toss through the noodles, steak, 4 tbsp light
soy sauce and 4 tbsp water. Stir-fry for 1 minute then scatter with red chilli and
coriander sprigs to serve.

the big smoke

breakfast

sundae morning ⓥ

serves 1 / ready in 5 minutes

Layer a Danone Activia 0% Fat
Vanilla yogurt in a glass with fresh
kiwi fruit and melon chunks and
top with 40g plain bite-size wheats
(Healthy Extra 'b').

lunch

minestrone soup ❄

serves 4 / ready in 30 minutes

Fry 1 chopped red onion, 1 crushed garlic
clove and 4 chopped back bacon rashers,
visible fat removed, in low-calorie cooking
spray until softened. Stir in 8 chopped
tomatoes, 100g dried macaroni, a drained
400g can butter beans and a little shredded
chard or kale. Pour in 800ml boiling chicken
stock, bring to the boil and simmer for
15 minutes. Season to taste.

dinner

kippers florentine

serves 2 / ready in 20 minutes

Peel 500g floury potatoes, cut into chunks and cook in boiling water over a high heat for
12-15 minutes. Drain and mash. Meanwhile, fill a deep frying pan with boiling water, place
over a high heat and bring to a simmer. Reduce the heat, swirl the water using a spoon
and crack in 2 eggs. Poach for 3-4 minutes or until the whites are set but the yolks are
still runny (see page 140). Remove the eggs with a slotted spoon and drain on kitchen
paper. Add 2 smoked kippers to the simmering water, heat for 2-3 minutes and transfer
to kitchen paper to drain. Meanwhile, pierce a large bag of washed baby leaf spinach a
few times and microwave on high for 1½ minutes or until just wilted (or wilt in a pan with
a little water over a low heat and drain). Put the spinach in a bowl and squeeze over the
juice of 1 lemon. Divide the mash and spinach between plates, top with kippers and
eggs, season to taste and serve hot with lemon wedges.

tagine genie

breakfast

fruity porridge Ⓥ

serves 1 / ready in 5 minutes

Microwave 40g plain porridge oats
(Healthy Extra 'b') with milk from
your Healthy Extra 'a' allowance
and top with fat-free natural Greek
yogurt, fresh pear slices and a
dusting of cinnamon.

lunch

chicken noodles

serves 1 / ready in 15 minutes

Cook dried noodles and toss with baby
sweetcorn, canned bamboo shoots, cooked
skinless chicken chunks and cooked sugar
snap peas. Make a dressing of lime juice, light
soy sauce, peeled and grated root ginger, red
chilli and fresh coriander and drizzle it over the
noodles. Follow with fresh pineapple chunks.

dinner

aubergine and chickpea tagine ❄ ⓥ vegan

serves 4 / ready in 25 minutes

Spray a large frying pan with low-calorie cooking spray and place over a medium heat. Add 1 large chopped onion, 2 tsp each garlic granules and ground cumin, and 1 tsp each ground ginger and ground cinnamon. Cook for 5 minutes then add 400g can chopped tomatoes and 400ml boiling vegetable stock and bring to the boil. Add 1 large aubergine, cut into chunks, and a drained 560g can new potatoes in water. Cover, reduce the heat to medium-low and simmer for 10 minutes. Stir in a drained 400g can chickpeas and cook for a few minutes then scatter with chopped fresh parsley and sprigs, season and serve with couscous.

fast & Free 35

budget bites

Good food doesn't have to cost a fortune, and these menu marvels all offer maximum flavour for the minimum cost.

country comforts

breakfast

spicy beans on toast

serves 1 / ready in 15 minutes

Fry sliced onion, mushrooms and garlic in low-calorie cooking spray for 10 minutes, add baked beans and paprika and heat through. Serve on 2 medium slices of wholemeal toast from a small 400g loaf (Healthy Extra 'b').

lunch

artichoke and spinach pasta

serves 1 / ready in 15 minutes

Cook and cool some dried pasta then mix with drained canned artichoke hearts, chopped red onion and tomato and a handful of baby spinach. Drizzle with fat-free vinaigrette. Follow with a ripe peach.

dinner

easy cottage pie ❄

serves 4 / ready in 45 minutes

Spray a frying pan with low-calorie cooking spray and place over a high heat. Add 500g lean beef mince (5% fat or less) and the sliced white part of 1 leek (save the green part) and fry for 5 minutes. Drain off any fat then stir in 400g can chopped tomatoes, 200ml boiling beef stock and 1 tsp dried thyme. Season to taste and bring to the boil, then cover and simmer for 25 minutes, stirring occasionally. Meanwhile, peel 500g potatoes and 1 swede and cut both into chunks. Boil for 15-20 minutes then mash with a little more stock. Add the sliced green part of the leek and 200g halved closed-cup mushrooms to the mince and cook for 3 minutes, then tip into an ovenproof dish. Spoon the mash on top, smooth over with a fork and brush with egg. Brown under a medium-high grill for 5 minutes and serve with Speed veg.

name that tuna

breakfast

blueberry 'cheesecake' crispbreads Ⓥ SP

serves 1 / ready in 10 minutes

Spread plain quark over a Healthy Extra 'b' serving of your favourite Ryvita crispbreads and top with fresh blueberries.

lunch

leek and potato soup
❄ Ⓥ **vegan** (without the fromage frais)

serves 1 / ready in 30 minutes

Fry 1 sliced leek, 1 peeled and chopped potato and 1 crushed garlic clove in low-calorie cooking spray until softened. Add 300ml boiling vegetable stock and bring to the boil. Simmer for 15 minutes, then whizz with a stick blender. Stir in chopped fresh chives and fat-free natural fromage frais and season to taste. Follow with a pear.

dinner

tuna and tomato pasta

serves 4 / ready in 20 minutes

Cook 400g dried pasta shapes according to the pack instructions. Meanwhile, spray a frying pan with low-calorie cooking spray and place over a medium heat. Finely chop 1 deseeded red chilli, 2 tomatoes and ½ red onion and fry for 10 minutes. Drain the pasta and return to the saucepan, adding the tomato mixture, 2 tbsp chopped fresh parsley and the zest and juice of 1½ unwaxed lemons. Season to taste and flake in 2 x 160g cans tuna chunks in spring water. Warm through for 2 minutes and stir in 25g rocket to serve.

budget bites 41

Latin love

breakfast

spaghetti brekkie

 vegan

serves 1 / ready in 10 minutes

Empty a can of spaghetti in tomato sauce into a pan, heat through and serve on 2 medium slices of wholemeal toast from a small 400g loaf (Healthy Extra 'b'). Follow with fresh papaya with lime juice squeezed over.

lunch

bubble and squeak cakes ❄ ⓥ

serves 1 / ready in 30 minutes

Peel and chop a potato or 2, boil with some green Speed veg such as cabbage or spinach until tender then drain and mash (you could use leftover mash and veg here). Season and shape into patties then bake with a couple of halved tomatoes at 200°C/fan 180°C/gas 6 for 15 minutes or until golden brown. Serve with fried eggs (see page 140).

dinner

mexican chicken and rice

serves 4 / ready in 50 minutes

Spray a large frying pan with low-calorie cooking spray and place over a high heat. Fry 8 skinless chicken thighs for 6-8 minutes to brown all over and set aside. Reduce the heat to low and fry 1 large chopped onion for 6-8 minutes. Stir in 3 sliced garlic cloves, 2 tsp ground cumin, 1 tsp sweet smoked paprika, 1 tsp dried chilli flakes and 300g dried basmati rice and fry for 1 minute. Spoon into an ovenproof dish and add 2 diced red peppers in brine from a jar and 650ml boiling chicken stock. Top with the chicken. Cover and bake at 190°C/fan 170°C/gas 5 for 20 minutes, then stir in a drained 400g can kidney beans and 200g frozen peas and bake for 10 minutes. Serve with salad and lime wedges.

feel the passion

breakfast

passion pot 🅥

serves 1 / ready in 5 minutes

Put fresh pineapple chunks, plenty of fat-free natural yogurt and 40g plain malt wheats cereal such as Shreddies (Healthy Extra 'b') into a bowl. Scoop over fresh passion fruit pulp to serve.

lunch

turkey and slaw

serves 1 / ready in 15 minutes

Mix lots of shredded cabbage, carrot and onion with fat-free natural fromage frais, black pepper and a pinch of mustard powder. Serve with slices of lean turkey, visible fat removed. Follow with a couple of satsumas.

dinner

chickpea, tomato and 'pesto' salad 🅥 🆂🅿

serves 4 / ready in 15 minutes

To make the 'pesto', put 2 small packs fresh basil leaves, 200g low-fat natural cottage cheese, 100ml cooled vegetable stock, 2 crushed garlic cloves, 1 tsp dried chilli flakes and the grated zest and juice of 1 unwaxed lemon in a small food processor and blitz until smooth (add a little water if needed). Season to taste. Halve 300g cherry tomatoes and put in a salad bowl with 2 drained 400g cans chickpeas and a small bag of watercress. Thinly slice 100g red radishes and add to the bowl along with 300g cooked and cooled green beans. Toss well and drizzle over the 'pesto' to serve.

rocky rodeo

breakfast

eggs and bacon on toast

serves 1 / ready in 10 minutes

Fry or poach a couple of eggs
(see page 140) and grill a couple
of back bacon rashers, visible
fat removed. Serve on 2 slices of
wholemeal toast from a small
400g loaf (Healthy Extra 'b').
Follow with fresh blackberries.

lunch

chinese tofu rice Ⓥ vegan

serves 1 / ready in 15 minutes

Cook some dried long-grain rice,
adding shredded pak choi and
broccoli florets for the last few minutes.
Meanwhile, cut plain/naturally smoked
tofu into chunks and fry in low-calorie
cooking spray until nicely browned,
turning occasionally. Drain the rice and
veg and mix in chopped spring onions,
lemon juice and soy sauce. Top with
the tofu chunks to serve.

dinner

cowboy hotpot ❄

serves 4 / ready in 45 minutes

Spray a large casserole pan with
low-calorie cooking spray and place
over a medium-high heat. Stir-fry
500g lean beef mince (5% fat or less)
for 5 minutes then drain off any fat and
add 2 chopped onions, 2 large peeled
and sliced carrots, 700g sliced waxy
potatoes and 250g runner beans, sliced
diagonally. Stir in 4 tbsp tomato purée
and 1.2 litres boiling beef stock, bring to
the boil and simmer for 30 minutes or
until tender. Stir in 2 x 400g cans drained
beans (eg. borlotti or black-eyed beans)
and a dash of Tabasco sauce and heat
through. Season to taste, divide between
bowls and scatter with chopped fresh
parsley to serve.

you are what you wheat

breakfast

baked oats Ⓥ SP

serves 1 / ready in 30 minutes

Mix 40g plain porridge oats
(Healthy Extra 'b'), 50ml milk from
your Healthy Extra 'a' allowance,
1 egg, 2 level tsp sweetener and a
little vanilla extract and cinnamon
in a small ovenproof dish. Bake
at 200°C/fan 180°C/gas 6 for
20-25 minutes then cool briefly
and top with plain quark and lots
of sliced fresh nectarine. Dust
with cinnamon.

lunch

ham and bean salad SP

serves 1 / ready in 5 minutes

Chop gherkins and lean ham, visible
fat removed, from a can or pack and
toss with drained canned mixed beans
or pulses in water, lots of grated carrot,
rocket and fat-free vinaigrette. Follow
with fresh raspberries and blueberries.

dinner

prawn tabbouleh

serves 4 / ready in 15 minutes

Put 250g dried bulgar wheat in a large heatproof bowl and pour in
400ml boiling water. Cover and set aside for 10-12 minutes or until the
water has been absorbed. Fluff up the grains with a fork and stir in
4 chopped tomatoes, 4 chopped or sliced spring onions, 1 diced
cucumber and ½ small pack each of chopped parsley, mint and dill.
Add the juice of 1 lemon and 400g cooked and peeled prawns, season
to taste and serve cold or at room temperature. Follow with a Müllerlight
Greek-style Lemon yogurt.

full of beans

breakfast

eggs with marmite soldiers

serves 1 / ready in 10 minutes

Boil 2 eggs to your liking – from 4 minutes for very soft-boiled to 10 minutes for very hard-boiled (see page 140). Toast 2 medium slices of wholemeal bread from a small 400g loaf (Healthy Extra 'b'), spread with Marmite and slice into soldiers. Serve with the eggs for dipping. Follow with fresh watermelon.

lunch

pimped-up jacket and beans vegan

serves 1 / ready in 1 hour

Bake a jacket potato at 200°C/fan 180°C/gas 6 for 1 hour or until tender with crispy skin. Fry chopped leek, crushed garlic and sliced mushrooms in low-calorie cooking spray until softened, then add baked beans and chilli powder and heat through. Slice open the potato, pile in the filling and serve with a sprinkling of chopped parsley and salad.

dinner

griddled chicken with squash wedges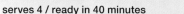

serves 4 / ready in 40 minutes

Peel and deseed 1 butternut squash and cut into thick chips. Arrange on
a baking tray lined with baking paper, spray with low-calorie cooking spray
and roast for 30 minutes. Meanwhile, wrap 4 skinless and boneless chicken
breasts in cling film and flatten with a mallet or rolling pin. Discard the cling
film, season, spray with low-calorie cooking spray and fry over a high heat
for 6-8 minutes each side or until cooked through. Scatter with parsley and
serve with the squash chips and extra Speed veg.

spaghetti junction

breakfast

scrambled eggs and beans Ⓥ

serves 1 / ready in 10 minutes

Scramble a few eggs and serve with baked beans. Follow with a Danone Activia 0% Fat Peach yogurt and fresh blueberries.

lunch

houmous spud Ⓥ

serves 1 / ready in 1 hour

Bake a jacket potato at 200°C/fan 180°C/gas 6 for 1 hour or until tender with crisp skin. Meanwhile, whizz together a drained 400g can chickpeas and add 2 tbsp fat-free natural yogurt, 2 tbsp lemon juice and a crushed garlic clove. Slice open the jacket, spoon in the houmous (you might have some left to enjoy another time) and serve with salad.

dinner

everyday spag bol ❄

serves 4 / ready in 40 minutes

Spray a large frying pan with low-calorie cooking spray and place over a high heat. Fry 500g lean beef mince (5% fat or less) for 5 minutes then transfer to a plate and drain off any fat. Spray the pan again, add 3 diced carrots and 200g sliced chestnut mushrooms and cook for 5 minutes. Return the mince to the pan, stir in 1½ tbsp tomato purée and cook for 2 minutes. Pour in 400g can chopped tomatoes with herbs, fill the empty can with water and add that too. Stir and bring to the boil then simmer for 20 minutes. Season to taste, scatter with chopped fresh parsley and serve hot with cooked dried spaghetti or pasta of your choice.

happy hunting ground

breakfast

masala omelette (V) (SP)

serves 1 / ready in 10 minutes

Beat a few eggs with sliced spring onions, chopped fresh coriander, chilli and a pinch of cumin. Fry in low-calorie cooking spray, roll up and serve with grilled tomatoes.

lunch

veggie dogs (V)

serves 1 / ready in 20 minutes

Cook 1 or 2 frozen Quorn Low Fat Sausages according to the pack instructions and fry sliced onion in low-calorie cooking spray. Use to fill a 60g wholemeal roll (Healthy Extra 'b'). Mix a little mustard powder with water and spoon on top. Follow with melon wedges.

dinner

hunter's chicken ❄ (SP)

serves 4 / ready in 50 minutes

Spray a casserole pan with low-calorie cooking spray and place over a high heat. Brown 4 skinned chicken thighs and 4 skinned drumsticks in batches and return them all to the pan. Reduce the heat to medium, add 1 chopped onion, 2 sliced celery sticks, 2 chopped garlic cloves, 300g halved button mushrooms and 2 chopped peppers and cook for 5 minutes. Stir in 100ml boiling chicken stock, 2 bay leaves and 2 x 400g cans cherry tomatoes plus their juice. Bring to the boil then simmer for 30 minutes, turning the chicken occasionally. Scatter with parsley and serve with swede mash.

some-fin for everyone

breakfast

orchard sunrise ⓥ

serves 1 / ready in 5 minutes

Chop 1-2 pears into chunks, dust with cinnamon or nutmeg and pile into a glass. Top with lots of fat-free natural yogurt and 45g Jordan's No Added Sugar Muesli (Healthy Extra 'b').

lunch

zesty chicken salad

serves 1 / ready in 10 minutes

Arrange cooked sliced skinless chicken, watercress, orange segments, sliced radishes and spring onions on a plate. Mix fat-free natural yogurt with mustard powder, chopped fresh parsley and dill and dollop over the salad to serve.

dinner

grilled pollock with garlic spinach

serves 4 / ready in 30 minutes

Spray a wide frying pan with low-calorie cooking spray and place over a medium-high heat. Gently fry 1 finely chopped onion for 5 minutes then add 400g chopped spinach, 150ml boiling chicken stock, the juice of ½ lemon and 2 crushed garlic cloves. Season and reduce the heat to medium. Stir in 200g halved cherry tomatoes and keep warm. Meanwhile, cook 4 pollock fillets under a medium-hot grill for 8-10 minutes or until cooked through, turning once. Gently flake the fish and put on to plates with the spinach and some rice (we made lemon rice, adding a pinch of turmeric and the juice of 1 lemon). Scatter with chopped fresh parsley and serve with lemon wedges.

make a hash of it

breakfast

fruity crunch

serves 1 / ready in 5 minutes

Mix fresh berries and grapes
into fat-free natural yogurt
and top with 45g bran flakes
(Healthy Extra 'b').

lunch

pea and mint soup
 vegan

serves 4 / ready in 30 minutes

Finely chop 1 onion, 2 celery sticks
and 2 garlic cloves and put into a
saucepan with 600g frozen peas and
1 litre boiling vegetable stock. Bring
to the boil and simmer for 20 minutes.
Add ½ small pack fresh mint and
blitz with a stick blender. Follow with
a banana.

dinner

ham and leek hash with eggs

serves 4 / ready in 40 minutes

Peel 800g potatoes and cut into chunks then boil for 5 minutes, drain and return to
the pan. Meanwhile, spray a casserole pan with low-calorie cooking spray and place
over a medium heat. Add 2 sliced leeks and a splash of water and cook for 5 minutes.
Add the potatoes and 200g chopped lean ham, visible fat removed, and fry to crisp
up a little. Stir in 1 tbsp dried parsley. Flatten the mixture lightly, spray with low-calorie
cooking spray and bake at 200°C/fan 180°C/gas 6 for 20 minutes or until browned.
Top with fried or poached eggs (see page 140) and serve with extra Speed veg.

it's cold outside

Outdoor chills mean mealtime thrills with these mouth-watering menus that will soothe your soul and warm your cockles!

spice up your life

breakfast

sardines on toast

serves 1 / ready in 5 minutes

Empty a can of sardines in tomato sauce into a pan, heat through and use to top 2 medium slices of wholemeal toast from a small 400g loaf (Healthy Extra 'b'). Scatter with parsley to serve. Follow with fresh grapefruit segments.

lunch

ham and mushroom muffins *SP*

serves 1 / ready in 30 minutes

Fry sliced mushrooms in low-calorie cooking spray then mix with a couple of sliced spring onions and chopped lean ham, visible fat removed. Tip the mixture into 2 holes of a silicone muffin tray, then divide 2 whisked eggs between the holes. Bake at 200°C/fan 180°C/gas 6 for 20-25 minutes and serve with salad. Follow with fresh blueberries.

dinner

piri-piri chicken bake

serves 4 / ready in 40 minutes

Make a few slashes in 4 skinless and boneless chicken breasts and rub in 3 chopped garlic cloves and 2 tbsp piri-piri seasoning. Put 4 quartered red onions, 2 sliced peppers and 200g cherry tomatoes in an ovenproof dish, top with the chicken and spray with low-calorie cooking spray. Toss well and roast at 220°C/fan 200°C/gas 7 for 25 minutes or until cooked through. Scatter with chopped fresh coriander and serve with cooked dried bulgar wheat and lemon wedges.

just joshing

breakfast

banana custard pot

serves 1 / ready in 5 minutes

Slice a banana and layer in a glass
with Müllerlight Banana & Custard
yogurt and lots of fresh berries.

lunch

ocean platter *SP*

serves 1 / ready in 5 minutes

Serve smoked salmon or trout
with cornichons, sliced cooked
beetroot from a jar, sliced tomatoes
and cucumber and lots of salad
leaves. Great with 4 Ryvita Original
crispbreads (Healthy Extra 'b').

dinner

lamb rogan josh ❄

serves 4 / ready in 2½ hours

Spray a casserole pan with low-calorie cooking spray and place over a high
heat. Cut 700g lean lamb leg steaks, visible fat removed, into bite-size chunks
and brown in the pan in batches. Set aside. Reduce the heat to medium-low,
add 2 sliced onions and cook for 10 minutes, stirring often. Add 3 chopped
garlic cloves, 2 tsp ground ginger, 4 tbsp curry powder (heat to your taste)
and 2 cinnamon sticks. Stir-fry for 2 minutes then return the lamb to the pan
and stir-fry for another 2 minutes. Add 2 x 400g cans chopped tomatoes,
200ml boiling beef stock and 2 red peppers, cut into chunks. Season to
taste and bring to the boil then cover and simmer over a low heat for 2 hours.
Scatter with coriander sprigs and serve with rice and chilli-spiced yogurt.

all about that bass

breakfast

hot wheats Ⓥ

serves 1 / ready in 5 minutes

Pour hot milk from your Healthy Extra 'a' allowance over 2 Shredded Wheat (Healthy Extra 'b') and top with fresh pineapple chunks.

lunch

hot dog jacket

serves 1 / ready in 1 hour

Bake a jacket potato at 200°C/fan 180°C/gas 6 for 1 hour or until tender with a crispy skin. Meanwhile, cook 1-2 Slimming World Syn-free Pork Sausages (or frozen Quorn Low Fat Sausages) according to the pack instructions and fry a small sliced onion in low-calorie cooking spray. Pack the sausages and onion into the jacket potato, top with made-up mustard powder or passata and serve with baked beans and salad.

dinner

spiced sea bass with puy lentils SP

serves 4 / ready in 30 minutes

Cook 275g dried Puy lentils in a pan of simmering water for 20 minutes or until tender.
Meanwhile, make a few slashes in 4 large sea bass fillets and sprinkle over 1 tbsp curry
powder and the juice of 2 limes. Season, place skin-side up on a baking tray sprayed
with low-calorie cooking spray and roast at 220°C/fan 200°C/gas 7 for 10 minutes
or until cooked through. At the same time, spray a wide frying pan with low-calorie
cooking spray and place over a medium heat. Add 2 chopped garlic cloves, 1 deseeded
shredded red chilli, 1 tsp ground cumin and 2cm piece root ginger, peeled and grated,
and stir-fry for 1-2 minutes. Add 1 chopped red onion, 100ml boiling chicken stock and
the drained lentils and bring to the boil. Spoon the lentils on to plates, top with the fish
and sprinkle with chopped fresh coriander. Serve with plenty of Speed veg.

it's cold outside 67

souped up

breakfast

peachy porridge Ⓥ SP

serves 1 / ready in 5 minutes

Heat 40g plain porridge oats (Healthy Extra 'b') with milk from your Healthy Extra 'a' allowance and top with lots of sliced fresh peach.

lunch

tomato soup ❄ Ⓥ SP

serves 2 / ready in 30 minutes

Chop 1 red onion, 1 carrot and 1 celery stick and stir-fry in low-calorie cooking spray for 5 minutes. Add a can of chopped tomatoes, 2 tbsp tomato purée, 1 level tbsp sweetener and 600ml boiling vegetable stock. Simmer for 15 minutes and blitz until smooth. Add a swirl of plain quark and scatter with small basil leaves. Follow with a few fresh plums.

dinner

paprika lamb stew ❄ SP

serves 4 / ready in 45 minutes

Spray a large casserole pan with low-calorie cooking spray and place over a high heat. Cut 600g lean lamb leg steaks, visible fat removed, into strips and fry with 6 halved shallots for 3 minutes. Add 2 courgettes, cut into bite-size chunks, and cook for 4 minutes. Stir in 1 tsp each ground cumin, cinnamon and sweet paprika plus 2 chopped garlic cloves and 3 peppers, cut into bite-size chunks. Reduce the heat to medium and cook for 5 minutes. Add 200ml boiling vegetable stock and 400g can cherry tomatoes plus their juices and season to taste. Bring to the boil then simmer for 20 minutes or until the veg are tender. Stir through a little fresh coriander and serve with lots of Speed veg. Follow with fresh cranberries and plain quark.

tea for two

breakfast

eggs on toast ⓥ ⓢⓟ

serves 1 / ready in 10 minutes

Lightly toast 2 medium slices
wholemeal bread from a small
400g loaf (Healthy Extra 'b').
Top with eggs fried in low-calorie
cooking spray and serve
with grilled tomatoes.

lunch

bangers and root mash

serves 1 / ready in 25 minutes

Peel and chop ½ swede and 1 parsnip
and boil over a high heat for 15-20 minutes or
until tender. Drain and mash. Meanwhile, cook
2-3 Slimming World Syn-free Pork Sausages
according to the pack instructions. Stir a little
fat-free natural fromage frais and chopped
fresh parsley into the mash and serve with the
sausages and mustard made up with mustard
powder. Serve with extra Speed veg and follow
with fresh melon wedges.

dinner

date night chicken dinner

serves 2 / ready in 1 hour

Put 500g halved new potatoes and 8 peeled shallots in an ovenproof dish. Cut
2 carrots and 1 red pepper into chunks and add to the tin along with 4 unpeeled
garlic cloves and 100ml boiling chicken stock. Squeeze over ½ lemon, spray with
low-calorie cooking spray and toss well. Cover with foil and roast at 200°C/fan
180°C/gas 6 for 15 minutes. Remove the foil, scatter over a few rosemary sprigs
and add 4 large skinless chicken thighs and 2 courgettes, cut into chunks. Tuck
a few lemon slices into the nooks and crannies and roast for 30 minutes or until
tender and cooked through. Scatter with chopped fresh parsley to serve.

a lotta borlotti

breakfast

potato and mushroom hash 🔱

serves 1 / ready in 20 minutes

Halve and parboil 300g new potatoes
then fry in low-calorie cooking spray with
mushrooms and fresh herbs. Squeeze
over some lemon juice and top with a
poached egg.

lunch

open salmon sandwich

serves 1 / ready in 5 minutes

Halve a 60g wholemeal roll (Healthy
Extra 'b') and spread with fat-free natural
fromage frais. Scatter over some chopped
dill and thinly sliced cucumber. Season and
top with smoked salmon and watercress.
Follow with watermelon wedges.

dinner

borlotti bean risotto 🔱 vegan

serves 4 / ready in 40 minutes

Put 1.2 litres vegetable stock in a saucepan over a low heat and bring to a simmer. Put
1 chopped onion, 1 crushed garlic clove, 1 tbsp each chopped fresh rosemary and
thyme, ½ tsp crushed fennel seeds and 3 tbsp of the stock in another saucepan over
a low heat. Cover and cook for 5 minutes then uncover and stir in 350g dried risotto
rice. Add the rest of the stock a ladleful at a time, stirring constantly and adding
another ladleful each time the last one has been absorbed. Cook for 25 minutes or
until almost all the stock has been used and the rice is creamy and just tender. Add
a drained, rinsed 400g can borlotti beans to the remaining stock, heat through and
stir it all into the rice. Stir in 3 tbsp chopped fresh parsley, season to taste and scatter
with a little more parsley. Serve with salad.

speak of the devil

breakfast

veggie fry-up ⓥ

serves 1 / ready in 20 minutes

Cook frozen Quorn Low-fat
Sausages and serve with fried eggs,
grilled tomatoes and plenty of baked
beans. Follow with an apple.

lunch

cheese 'n' onion jacket ⓥ

serves 1 / ready in 1 hour

Cook a jacket potato at 200°C/fan 180°C/
gas 6 for 1 hour or until tender with a crispy
skin. Grate or dice a Healthy Extra 'a'
portion of your favourite cheese, mix with
2 sliced spring onions and fat-free natural
fromage frais. Slice the potato open, pile in
the filling and serve with salad.

dinner

devilled mackerel with orange and fennel salad

serves 4 / ready in 25 minutes

Thinly slice 1 red onion and place in a bowl with the segments of 2 large
oranges and 2 thinly sliced fennel bulbs. Squeeze over the juice of
2 lemons, season to taste and set aside. Meanwhile, mix 3 tbsp fat-free
natural yogurt, 1 tbsp curry powder, 1 tsp mustard powder and 2 tsp red
wine vinegar. Lay 8 mackerel fillets on a board and, using a sharp knife,
slash the skin of each fillet a few times. Rub the devilling mixture over the
fish and cook under a medium-hot grill for 6-8 minutes or until cooked
through, turning once. Serve hot with the fennel salad.

welsh wonders

breakfast

appley ever after weetabix (V) (SP)

serves 1 / ready in 5 minutes

Pour warm milk from your Healthy Extra 'a' allowance over 2 wholewheat biscuits such as Weetabix (Healthy Extra 'b') and pile sliced fresh apple on top.

lunch

pizza omelette (SP)

serves 1 / ready in 15 minutes

Fry a few beaten eggs in a pan sprayed with low-calorie cooking spray to make an omelette. When almost set, scatter with chopped tomatoes, chunks of lean ham, visible fat removed, and dried oregano (or your own favourite Free pizza toppings). Sprinkle with black pepper and finish under the grill. Scatter with fresh basil or oregano leaves and serve with salad.

dinner

glamorgan sausages (V) vegan (without the egg)

serves 4 / ready in 40 minutes, plus chilling

Drain 2 x 400g cans cannellini beans and tip into a food processor with 1 roughly chopped small red onion, ½ pack fresh parsley, 4 grated carrots, 2 tsp dried mixed herbs and a splash of Tabasco. Season, pulse to combine and transfer to a bowl. Divide into 12 portions and shape into sausages, then brush with egg and chill for at least 3 hours. Bake them at 200°C/fan 180°C/gas 6 for 15-20 minutes or until golden. Meanwhile, fry 6 peeled and sliced shallots in a large pan sprayed with low-calorie cooking spray over a medium heat. When nearly cooked, add 200ml boiling vegetable stock and 1 tbsp balsamic vinegar and cook until the water has mostly gone. Serve the sausages hot with the shallot gravy, mashed potatoes and Speed veg.

one for the pot

breakfast

kippers and eggs

serves 1 / ready in 15 minutes

Grill some kippers for 10 minutes and serve with a few eggs, scrambled with a splash of milk from your Healthy Extra 'a' allowance. Follow with a ripe nectarine.

lunch

picchi-pacchi pasta

serves 1 / ready in 15 minutes

Fry garlic, chopped plum tomatoes, red chilli and spring onions in low-calorie cooking spray for just 1-2 minutes. Stir through cooked dried pasta plus a handful of rocket.

dinner

steak hotpot ❄

serves 4 / ready in 3 hours

Roughly chop 3 large onions, 2 carrots and 8 large tomatoes, and finely chop 4 garlic cloves. Spray a casserole dish with low-calorie cooking spray and layer one-third of the onions and half of the carrots, tomatoes and garlic. Sprinkle over 1 tsp dried mixed herbs and add a layer of 4 lean beef braising steaks, visible fat removed. Season, sprinkle with 1 tsp dried mixed herbs and add the rest of the carrots, tomatoes and garlic. Scatter the rest of the onions and pour in 200ml boiling beef stock. Top with 4 large peeled and thickly sliced floury potatoes and sprinkle with dried parsley. Cover and cook at 180°C/fan 160°C/gas 4 for 2 hours then remove the lid, spray with low-calorie cooking spray and cook for 20-25 minutes. Leave to stand for 10 minutes and serve with Speed veg.

pearly king

breakfast

toffee apple porridge

serves 1 / ready in 5 minutes

Cook 40g plain porridge oats
(Healthy Extra 'b') with milk from
your Healthy Extra 'a' allowance
or water. Stir in a Müllerlight
Toffee yogurt and top with
sliced fresh apple.

lunch

crab noodles

serves 1 / ready in 10 minutes

Cook dried noodles and cool in cold water.
Drain a can of white crabmeat and a can
of sliced water chestnuts and stir into the
noodles along with some chilli, spring onions,
lime zest and juice and a little black pepper.
Follow with a bowl of grapes.

dinner

chicken and pearl barley casserole ❄

serves 4 / ready in 1 hour

Cut 2 large onions, 3 celery sticks and ½ peeled swede or squash into bite-size chunks
and pop it all into a casserole pan. Add 8 large skinless chicken thighs, 300g baby or
Chantenay carrots, 2 chopped garlic cloves, 3 sliced leeks, 100g dried pearl barley,
10 peppercorns, 1 bay leaf and 2 tsp dried mixed herbs. Add 1.5 litres boiling chicken
stock, bring to the boil and simmer for 45 minutes, stirring occasionally. Lift out the
chicken and shred the meat, discarding the bones. Return the chicken to the pan,
heat for 5 minutes and scatter with chopped fresh parsley to serve.

bring home the bacon

breakfast

turkey bacon, mushrooms and tomatoes *SP*

serves 1 / ready in 10 minutes

Cook portobello mushrooms, halved tomatoes and turkey bacon rashers in a grill pan over a medium heat until nicely charred. Meanwhile, put 3 tbsp balsamic vinegar and 2 level tsp sweetener in a pan and simmer until reduced by half. Put the bacon, tomatoes and mushrooms on a plate, drizzle with the balsamic vinegar and scatter with basil leaves.

lunch

scandinavian salmon

serves 1 / ready in 15 minutes

Spray a salmon fillet with low-calorie cooking spray, season and grill for 10 minutes or until cooked, turning once. Meanwhile, mix grated cucumber with fat-free natural fromage frais, fresh chives and black pepper. Serve the salmon on a bed of watercress with the cucumber mixture on top. Follow with a couple of tangerines or clementines.

dinner

butternut squash lasagne *V*

serves 4 / ready in 1½ hours

Put 700g passata in a saucepan and add 227g can chopped tomatoes, 1 finely chopped onion, 600g small butternut squash chunks and 2 red peppers, cut into bite-size chunks. Add fresh basil and bring to the boil, then simmer for 10 minutes. Meanwhile, mix 300g plain quark, 2 tsp dried sage, 1 tsp dried chilli flakes, 400g low-fat natural cottage cheese and 1 large egg. Season to taste and mix well. Layer one-third of the tomato sauce in a large ovenproof dish, add 3 dried lasagne sheets and one-third of the cottage cheese mixture. Repeat the layers twice more and top with 3 more lasagne sheets. Cover with foil and bake at 180°C/fan 160°C/gas 4 for 35 minutes. Beat 2 eggs with 250g fat-free natural Greek yogurt, spread over the lasagne and bake uncovered for 20 minutes. Stand for 10 minutes and serve with salad.

cod job

breakfast

overnight berry oats 🅥

**serves 1 / ready in 5 minutes,
plus overnight chilling**

Layer 40g plain porridge oats (Healthy
Extra 'b') with a Danone Activia 0% Fat
Raspberry yogurt. Chill overnight then
stir it up and top with fresh blueberries.

lunch

chicken and bacon pasta

serves 1 / ready in 20 minutes

Stir 1 shredded cooked skinless chicken
breast and 2 cooked back bacon rashers,
visible fat removed, into cooked and
cooled dried pasta. Add some cooked
and sliced runner beans and shredded
lettuce and drizzle with fat-free vinaigrette.

dinner

cod and bean bake

serves 4 / ready in 45 minutes

Put 4 chopped peppers, 1 diced courgette and 1 red onion, cut
into wedges, in a deep roasting tin. Spray with low-calorie cooking
spray and roast at 220°C/fan 200°C/gas 7 for 15 minutes or until
softened and charred at the edges. Stir in 500g passata, 1 tsp
balsamic vinegar, 4 chopped garlic cloves, a pinch of dried chilli
flakes (or more if you like) and a drained 400g can butter beans.
Make 4 wells in the mix and nestle a cod fillet into each. Season to
taste and roast for 15 minutes or until the cod is cooked. Scatter
with basil leaves and serve with rice.

the roast with the most

breakfast

orange pot (V)

serves 1 / ready in 5 minutes

Stir a little orange essence into some fat-free natural yogurt, then layer in a glass with the segments of 1 orange or 2-3 satsumas, finishing with a few more segments on top.

lunch

carrot and ginger soup ❄ (V) (SP)

serves 4 / ready in 35 minutes

Put 1 litre boiling vegetable stock and 7 roughly chopped carrots in a saucepan. Chop 1 onion, 2 celery sticks, 2 garlic cloves and 1cm piece peeled root ginger and add to the pan. Bring to the boil then simmer for 20 minutes. Season, blitz with a stick blender and swirl in some plain quark. Serve with a 60g wholemeal roll (Healthy Extra 'b').

dinner

balsamic pork roast ❄ (SP)

serves 4 / ready in 45 minutes

Put 2 lean pork fillets (about 400g each) in a roasting tin and rub in 4 tbsp balsamic vinegar, 2 tbsp Schwartz Steak Seasoning and 2 tbsp finely chopped fresh rosemary. Make small slits all over the pork and stuff with sliced garlic. Pour 200ml boiling chicken stock around the pork, scatter 20 peeled and halved or quartered shallots around the tray and roast for 20-25 minutes at 220°C/fan 200°C/gas 7 or until cooked. Rest and slice the pork, garnish with rosemary sprigs and serve hot with the shallots, a big pile of swede mash and some green Speed veg.

feelin' hot, hot, hot

Keep cool when the sun is shining by serving up lighter
meals that are every bit as delicious and satisfying.

tex appeal

breakfast

citrus start ⓥ

serves 1 / ready in 10 minutes

Peel a grapefruit and an orange and chop into bite-size chunks. Layer in a bowl or glass with fat-free natural Greek yogurt and top with 45g Dorset Cereals Simply Delicious Muesli (Healthy Extra 'b').

lunch

smoked salmon sweet potato jacket

serves 1 / ready in 50 minutes

Bake a sweet potato at 190°C/fan 170°C/gas 5 for 45 minutes or until tender. Meanwhile, mix sliced smoked salmon with fat-free natural yogurt, dill, lemon juice and a little seasoning. Slice open the sweet potato, pile in the filling and serve with Speed vegetables.

dinner

tex-mex steak with salsa ⓢⓟ

serves 4 / ready in 20 minutes

Mix 2 tsp chilli powder, 2 tsp cumin seeds and a little seasoning and rub all over 2 rump, sirloin or fillet steaks, visible fat removed. Spray a griddle or frying pan with low-calorie cooking spray and place over a high heat. Fry 2 sliced red onions for a few minutes then transfer to a plate. Add the steaks to the pan, cook to your liking (2 minutes each side for rare, 3 for medium and 4 for well done) and set aside with the onions. Make a salsa by mixing 2 chopped tomatoes, the juice of 2 limes, 1 tbsp tomato purée, 1 tsp cumin seeds, 2 chopped red peppers and 2 drained 400g cans black beans. Slice the steaks, arrange on top of the salsa along with the onions and serve with shredded lettuce.

fish for compliments

breakfast

green eggs and ham *SP*

serves 1 / ready in 10 minutes

Shred a big handful of fresh spinach
then scramble a few eggs in a pan,
adding the spinach halfway. Pile on to
2 medium slices of wholemeal toast
from a small 400g loaf (Healthy Extra
'b') and top with diced tomatoes and a
slice of lean ham, visible fat removed.

lunch

punchy potato salad *V*

serves 1 / ready in 15 minutes

Mix fat-free natural fromage frais
with a little mustard powder and
chopped fresh chives. Stir through
sliced spring onions, chopped celery
and apple, boiled baby potatoes and
shredded lettuce. Follow with a couple
of satsumas.

dinner

tuna kebabs

serves 4 / ready in 20 minutes, plus marinating

Mix 4 tbsp light soy sauce, 2 tbsp rice wine vinegar (or sherry vinegar),
2cm piece fresh root ginger, peeled and finely grated, 1 tbsp Worcestershire
sauce and a pinch of sweetener in a wide bowl. Cut 4 thick tuna steaks into
bite-size chunks and add to the bowl. Stir to coat well, cover and chill for
30 minutes. Cut 2 courgettes and 3 yellow peppers into bite-size chunks and
thread on to 12 skewers (soaked if wooden) along with the tuna chunks and
8 spring onions, cut into short lengths. Spray with low-calorie cooking spray
and barbecue or grill for 6-7 minutes, turning once. Sprinkle with chilli powder
or paprika and serve hot with rice, lemon wedges and extra Speed vegetables.

been there, done tzat

breakfast

blueberry brekkie Ⓥ ⑤Ⓟ

serves 1 / ready in 5 minutes

Pour milk from your Healthy Extra 'a' allowance over 45g blueberry-filled wheat biscuits (Healthy Extra 'b'). Top with fresh blueberries.

lunch

med veg pasta Ⓥ

serves 1 / ready in 15 minutes

Cook some dried pasta and drain well. Meanwhile, spray diced red pepper, aubergine and courgette and sliced red onion with low-calorie cooking spray and fry for 5 minutes or until tender. Toss the veg through the pasta with a little balsamic vinegar and chopped fresh basil.

dinner

spicy turkey burgers, tzatziki and chips

serves 4 / ready in 30 minutes

Finely slice 4 spring onions and mix half with 500g lean turkey mince (5% fat or less), 1 tbsp oyster sauce and 4 tbsp chopped fresh coriander. Form into 4 burgers (we used chef's rings for a neat shape) and cook under a high grill for 6-7 minutes on each side or until cooked. Meanwhile, make the tzatziki by mixing ½ diced cucumber, 2 deseeded and finely chopped tomatoes, 200g fat-free natural yogurt, 2 tbsp chopped fresh mint, ¼ tsp Tabasco and the remaining spring onions. Serve the burgers with the tzatziki, Slimming World chips (see page 106) and salad.

feelin' hot, hot, hot

keep calm and curry on

breakfast

bacon and mushroom bap *SP*

serves 1 / ready in 10 minutes

Grill a portobello mushroom and 2 back bacon rashers, visible fat removed, and use to fill a 60g wholemeal roll (Healthy Extra 'b') spread with warmed passata. Follow with fresh strawberries.

lunch

summer prawn salad

serves 1 / ready in 15 minutes

Toss cooked and peeled prawns with lemon juice, chopped fresh parsley and black pepper. Enjoy with a salad of cooked dried bulgar wheat, peppers, broad beans, cherry tomatoes and rocket. Follow with fresh cherries.

dinner

saag aloo gobi ❄ Ⓥ vegan

serves 4 / ready in 35 minutes

Steam or boil 500g peeled potato chunks and 1 medium cauliflower, broken into florets, for 8-10 minutes. Spray a large frying pan with low-calorie cooking spray and place over a medium-high heat. Add 1 thinly sliced onion, 2 chopped garlic cloves, 1cm piece root ginger, peeled and grated, and 2 tsp each cumin seeds and black mustard seeds and fry for 1-2 minutes. Add the cauliflower and potatoes and stir-fry for 6-8 minutes, then add 1 tbsp curry powder and 300g passata. Pour in 400ml boiling vegetable stock, bring to the boil and simmer for 5 minutes. Stir in 250g spinach until wilted then scatter with coriander sprigs and serve with rice.

go the whole hog

breakfast

poached eggs and summer soldiers 🍃 SP

serves 1 / ready in 10 minutes

Halve and lightly toast a 60g wholemeal roll (Healthy Extra 'b'). Serve with poached eggs (see page 140) and steamed asparagus tips to dip into the eggs.

lunch

coronation chicken pasta

serves 1 / ready in 15 minutes

Cook some dried pasta shapes, drain well and mix with fat-free natural yogurt, coriander and a little mild curry powder. Stir in cooked skinless chicken chunks and serve with a kachumber salad (roughly chopped red onion, tomato, cucumber, coriander and lime juice). Follow with thinly sliced fresh pineapple 'carpaccio' sprinkled with fresh mint, pomegranate seeds and a dollop of fat-free natural yogurt.

dinner

harissa pork bake SP

serves 4 / ready in 40 minutes

Cut 2 lean pork fillets (about 400g each), visible fat removed, into thick slices and rub in 2 tbsp harissa spices and some black pepper. Set aside. Tip 700g prepared squash chunks into an ovenproof dish and toss with 3 tbsp brine from a jar of roasted red peppers plus another 1 tbsp harissa spices. Roast at 200°C/fan 180°C/gas 6 for 15 minutes then increase the heat to 220°C/fan 200°C/gas 7. Drain the jar of peppers, tear the peppers into chunks and add to the dish. Arrange the pork on top and roast for 10 minutes or until cooked, then scatter with chopped fresh coriander to serve.

prawn cracker

breakfast

summer fruit tower

serves 1 / ready in 5 minutes

Layer fresh raspberries, Müllerlight
Raspberry and Cranberry yogurt
and 45g Jordan's No Added
Sugar Natural Muesli (Healthy
Extra 'b') in a glass.

lunch

roast tomato and bean pasta

 vegan

serves 1 / ready in 25 minutes

Sprinkle halved cherry tomatoes with
chopped rosemary and garlic and roast
at 220°C/fan 200°C/gas 7 for 20 minutes.
Add to cooked dried pasta shapes along
with baby sweetcorn, drained canned
aduki beans, ½ finely chopped red onion,
watercress, fresh basil and balsamic vinegar.

dinner

herbed prawn omelette *SP*

makes 1 / ready in 15 minutes

Mix together 2 finely chopped spring onions, 1 tbsp each finely chopped fresh chives, dill and parsley, 200g cooked and peeled prawns and 2 tbsp plain quark. Season and set aside. Spray a small frying pan with low-calorie cooking spray, place over a high heat and add 3 beaten eggs. As soon as the eggs begin to set, spoon the prawn and herb mixture down the centre of the omelette, roll it over to enclose the filling and cook for 1-2 minutes or until warmed through. Serve hot with salad.

feelin' hot, hot, hot 101

have a rice day

breakfast

sausage sandwich *SP*

serves 1 / ready in 20 minutes

Cook 2 Slimming World Syn-free Pork Sausages according to the pack instructions. Halve lengthways, sandwich between 2 medium slices of wholemeal toast from a small 400g loaf (Healthy Extra 'b') and serve with grilled tomatoes. Follow with an apple.

lunch

crunchy chicken and potato salad

serves 1 / ready in 15 minutes

Boil and halve some new potatoes, drain and tip into a bowl with sliced hard-boiled eggs, cooked skinless chicken chunks and some chopped celery, red pepper and cucumber. Mix fat-free natural fromage frais with a pinch of mustard powder, sliced spring onions and a splash of white wine vinegar and drizzle over the salad. Season to taste.

dinner

spring risotto *V* [vegan]

serves 4 / ready in 50 minutes

Bring 1 litre vegetable stock to the boil in a large saucepan over a high heat. Reduce the heat to medium, add 200g halved baby carrots and cook for 5 minutes. Add 200g each frozen peas, shelled broad beans and halved green beans and asparagus tips. Cook for 5 minutes then lift the veg into a bowl with a slotted spoon (pod the cooled broad beans if you like) and keep the stock simmering. Spray another large saucepan with low-calorie cooking spray and place over a medium heat. Add 4 sliced spring onions, 2 chopped garlic cloves and 1 sliced leek, then cook for 2 minutes and stir in 300g dried risotto rice. Add the stock a ladleful at a time and cook over a low heat, stirring occasionally and adding more stock once each ladleful has been absorbed. When the rice is done, stir in the boiled veg and serve with fresh mint sprigs.

call me al-fresco

breakfast

shakshuka

serves 1-2 / ready in 30 minutes

Spray a wide pan with low-calorie cooking spray and fry sliced onion and red peppers over a medium heat for 10 minutes. Add garlic, ground cumin and cayenne pepper and cook for 1 minute then add tomato purée and chopped tomatoes. Simmer for 10 minutes then make 2 wells in the mixture, crack in 2 eggs and cook to your liking (see page 140). Scatter with chopped fresh coriander to serve.

lunch

fruit 'n' veg rice

serves 1 / ready in 15 minutes

Cook some dried rice according to the pack instructions. Drain well and mix in drained canned beans of your choice, a squeeze of lemon juice, chopped spring onions, cucumber, cherry tomatoes, apricots and fresh coriander. Follow with fresh figs.

dinner

alfresco chicken salad

serves 4 / ready in 40 minutes

Spray 4 skinless and boneless chicken breasts with low-calorie cooking spray, put on a baking tray and sprinkle with the zest of 1 unwaxed lemon. Roast at 200°C/fan 180°C/gas 6 for 20 minutes or until cooked through. Meanwhile, pour enough boiling water over 200g dried couscous to just cover and leave to soak for 10 minutes. Put 100g chopped rocket, 100g drained cornichons, ½ chopped red onion, 200g halved cherry tomatoes and a drained 400g can artichoke hearts in water, quartered, into a large salad bowl. Make a dressing from the juice of 1 lemon, 2 crushed garlic cloves, 2 tsp balsamic vinegar and 1 tsp mustard powder mixed with 2 tsp water. Dice the chicken, fluff up the couscous and add both to the salad, then drizzle over the dressing.

quiche me quick

breakfast

sautéed mushrooms on toast ⓥ vegan ⓢⓟ

serves 1 / ready in 15 minutes

Fry mushrooms in a pan sprayed with low-calorie cooking spray, stir in a little crushed garlic and scatter with parsley. Add lemon juice and seasoning and serve on 2 medium slices of wholemeal toast from a small 400g loaf (Healthy Extra 'b').

lunch

chicken and quinoa

serves 1 / ready in 15 minutes

Cook some dried quinoa according to the pack instructions. Fluff up the grains and top with cooked skinless and boneless chicken breast, chopped cucumber, cooked beetroot from a jar and fresh mint. Follow with fresh blackberries.

dinner

crustless ratatouille quiche and chips ⓥ

serves 4 / ready in 50 minutes

Peel 1kg floury potatoes, slice into chips and parboil for 10 minutes. Meanwhile, line a 22cm square baking tray with non-stick baking paper and spray with low-calorie cooking spray. Put 1 sliced onion, 2 diced red peppers and 1 large diced aubergine in the tray. Season, toss well and roast at 200°C/fan 180°C/gas 6 for 20 minutes. Drain the chips, transfer to another baking tray and roast for 20-25 minutes. Beat 8 eggs, stir through a few shredded basil leaves and pour over the roasted vegetables. Sprinkle with 1 tsp dried oregano and bake for 15 minutes. Stand for 5 minutes then slice and serve with the chips and lots of salad.

abra-kebab-ra

breakfast
on the go ⓥ
serves 1 / ready in 5 minutes

Take breakfast to work – pack a Hi-fi bar (½ x Healthy Extra 'b'), watermelon wedges and a Danone Light & Free Strawberry Sensation yogurt.

lunch
tuna jacket
serves 1 / ready in 1 hour

Bake a jacket potato at 200°C/ fan 180°C/gas 6 for 1 hour or until tender with a crisp skin. Meanwhile, drain a can of tuna in spring water and mix with sliced spring onion, drained canned sweetcorn, fat-free natural fromage frais and black pepper. Slice open the potato, pile in the filling and enjoy with a big salad. Follow with a Hi-fi bar (½ x Healthy Extra 'b').

dinner
lamb kebabs with pasta salad
serves 4 / ready in 25 minutes, plus marinating

Mix the zest and juice of 2 unwaxed lemons, 3 crushed garlic cloves, 2 tsp each dried mint and oregano and a little seasoning in a wide bowl. Cut 600g lean lamb leg steaks, visible fat removed, into chunks, add to the bowl and marinate for at least 30 minutes. Meanwhile, cook 350g dried pasta shapes according to the pack instructions, drain and mix with 1 diced cucumber, 200g quartered cherry tomatoes, 1 roughly chopped small red onion, 2 tbsp fat-free vinaigrette and 1 tsp dried oregano. Thread the lamb on to 8 metal skewers and cook under a medium-high grill for 7-8 minutes, turning occasionally. Serve with the pasta (this is also great with tzatziki – see page 95). Follow with fresh plums.

stand by your mango

breakfast
herby omelette
serves 1 / ready in 10 minutes

Fry beaten eggs in low-calorie cooking
spray, adding a couple of chopped
tomatoes and a mixture of chopped
fresh herbs, such as parsley, basil and
chives. Serve with baked beans. Follow
with fresh blueberries.

lunch
bbq steak 🄢🄟
serves 1 / ready in 10 minutes

Rub a little Schwartz Steak Seasoning
into your favourite lean steak, visible fat
removed, spray with low-calorie cooking
spray and barbecue or griddle to your
liking (2 minutes each side for rare,
3 minutes for medium and 4 minutes
for well done). Serve with barbecued or
griddled mushrooms and courgettes.

dinner
spiced salmon with mango couscous
serves 4 / ready in 25 minutes, plus marinating

Spray a roasting tin with low-calorie cooking spray and add 4 skinless salmon fillets.
Mix 4 tsp Cajun spices and the juice of 2 limes, rub over the fish and marinate in the
fridge for 30 minutes. Roast at 200°C/fan 180°C/gas 6 for 15 minutes. Meanwhile,
just cover 300g dried couscous with boiling water, cover with cling film and leave to
absorb for 10 minutes. Fluff up the grains and stir through 8 sliced spring onions,
1 diced cucumber, 1 diced green pepper, the zest and juice of 1 unwaxed lemon,
200g diced fresh mango and some chopped fresh coriander. Put the fish on top
and serve with coriander sprigs, lime wedges and salad.

posh nosh

Take your seat at the chef's table for these everyday breakfasts, lunches and dinners with a little added sparkle.

raise the steaks

breakfast

cheat's eggs benedict
serves 1 / ready in 10 minutes

Top a halved and toasted 60g wholemeal roll (Healthy Extra 'b') with lean ham, visible fat removed, and poached eggs (see page 140). Add dollops of plain quark or fat-free natural fromage frais to serve. Follow with fresh raspberries.

lunch

chicken and nectarine pasta
serves 1 / ready in 15 minutes

Cook dried pasta shapes and mix with sliced cooked skinless chicken breast, sliced fresh nectarines or peaches, drained canned haricot beans and fat-free vinaigrette. Add black pepper and scatter over a few basil leaves.

dinner

steak au poivre
serves 4 / ready in 30 minutes

Drain a 560g can new potatoes in water, tip the spuds into a baking tray and spray with low-calorie cooking spray. Sprinkle over 1 tsp dried rosemary, season to taste and roast at 220°C/fan 200°C/gas 7 for 10-12 minutes. Meanwhile, rub 4 tbsp crushed black peppercorns over 4 beef steaks, visible fat removed, and spray with low-calorie cooking spray. Fry in a large griddle or frying pan over a high heat (2 minutes each side for rare, 3 for medium and 4 for well done), then lift out of the pan and cover with foil. Pour 200ml boiling beef stock, 1 tsp beef stock concentrate and 1 chopped garlic clove into the pan and boil for 2 minutes. Remove from the heat and stir in 4 tbsp fat-free natural fromage frais. Meanwhile, wilt 400g spinach in boiling water, drain well and stir in some seasoning and 150g fat-free natural fromage frais. Spoon the sauce over the steaks, garnish with tarragon sprigs and serve with the roasties, creamed spinach and extra Speed vegetables.

tikka chance

breakfast

sunshine crunch

serves 1 / ready in 5 minutes

Cut fresh apricots into wedges and layer in a glass with 2 crumbled wholewheat biscuits such as Weetabix (Healthy Extra 'b') and fat-free natural yogurt.

lunch

spanish tortilla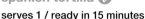

serves 1 / ready in 15 minutes

In a frying pan, cook chopped red onion, sliced canned new potatoes and sliced roasted red peppers in brine from a jar. Pour in a few beaten eggs, season and sprinkle with dried thyme. Cook until almost set then finish under the grill and serve with Speed vegetables.

dinner

chicken tikka

serves 4 / ready in 25 minutes, plus marinating

Mix the juice of 1 lime, 150g fat-free natural yogurt and 2 tbsp curry powder (heat to your taste) in a large shallow bowl. Cut 4 skinless and boneless chicken breasts into large chunks, add to the yogurt and toss well. Cover and chill for at least 3 hours. Thread the chunks on to 8 skewers (soaked if wooden), spray with low-calorie cooking spray and cook on a griddle or frying pan over a medium heat for 6-8 minutes or until cooked and charred. Serve hot with rice, lime wedges and a chunky salad.

tips from the top

breakfast
french toast

serves 1 / ready in 10 minutes

Dip 2 medium slices of wholemeal toast from a small 400g loaf (Healthy Extra 'b') in beaten eggs and fry both sides in low-calorie cooking spray until browned. Top with a dollop of fat-free natural fromage frais, sliced banana and cinnamon.

lunch
chicken waldorf jacket

serves 1 / ready in 1 hour

Bake a jacket potato at 200°C/fan 180°C/gas 6 for 1 hour or until tender with a crispy skin. Mix chunks of cooked skinless chicken with sliced celery and apple, halved red grapes and fat-free natural fromage frais. Slice open the potato, pile in the filling and serve with salad.

dinner
pasta with salmon and asparagus tips

serves 4 / ready in 20 minutes

Put 4 skinless salmon fillets on to 4 pieces of kitchen foil and squeeze over a little lemon juice. Scrunch up the parcels and roast at 200°C/fan 180°C/gas 6 for 12 minutes. Meanwhile, cook 500g dried pasta shapes according to the pack instructions, adding 200g asparagus tips and 200g long-stem broccoli for the last 4 minutes. Drain well. Mix 100g fat-free natural fromage frais with the juice of ½ lemon and stir into the pasta and vegetables. Flake in the salmon, season to taste and serve with lemon wedges. Follow with a couple of plums.

enjoy a breakfiesta

breakfast

the full mexican

serves 1 / ready in 25 minutes

Parboil some diced potatoes and fry in low-calorie cooking spray with dried oregano, smoked paprika, sliced red and yellow peppers and 2 sliced back bacon rashers, visible fat removed. Crack in an egg and fry to your liking (see page 140). Top with chopped fresh coriander to serve.

lunch

chef's chicken salad *SP*

serves 1 / ready in 15 minutes

Mix shredded lettuce and carrot with sliced tomato and cucumber. Top with a big dollop of low-fat natural cottage cheese, cooked skinless chicken chunks and a sprinkling of chopped fresh chives. Follow with fresh strawberries.

dinner

veggie paella *V* vegan

serves 4 / ready in 50 minutes

Spray a large frying pan with low-calorie cooking spray and fry 2 finely chopped onions over a medium heat for 5 minutes. Add 4 chopped garlic cloves, 2 diced peppers, 2 diced carrots and 2 diced tomatoes and cook for 5 minutes. Stir in 300g dried paella rice, 1 bay leaf, 1 tbsp smoked paprika and a pinch of saffron or turmeric. Pour in 900ml boiling vegetable stock and bring to the boil. Cover, reduce the heat to very low and cook for 20 minutes or until tender and the liquid has been absorbed, adding 100g frozen peas for the last 5 minutes. Remove from the heat and leave to stand for 10 minutes, still covered. Scatter with parsley and serve with lemon wedges. Follow with fresh pineapple chunks.

dinner from the deep

breakfast

bacon frittata *SP*

serves 1 / ready in 20 minutes

Spray a frying pan with low-calorie cooking spray and fry diced courgette and 2 chopped back bacon rashers, visible fat removed, until golden. Add halved cherry tomatoes, pour in a few beaten eggs and cook until set, finishing under the grill. Scatter with fresh basil to serve.

lunch

margherita melt *V* *SP*

serves 1 / ready in 10 minutes

Split and toast a 60g wholemeal roll (Healthy Extra 'b') then top each half with tomato purée and sliced red onion. Divide 40g grated reduced-fat Cheddar (Healthy Extra 'a') between the two halves and grill until melted. Serve with salad. Follow with a couple of satsumas.

dinner

roast halibut with fennel and balsamic tomatoes

serves 4 / ready in 30 minutes

Thinly slice 1 fennel bulb and 1 red onion and scatter in a roasting tin with 2 deseeded and sliced red chillies. Pour over 150ml boiling chicken stock and roast at 200°C/fan 180°C/gas 6 for 10 minutes. Add 200g cherry tomatoes and roast for a further 5 minutes. Drizzle with 3 tbsp balsamic vinegar, place 4 skinless halibut fillets on top and roast for 10-12 minutes or until the fish is just cooked through. Season to taste, scatter over a little fresh dill and 2 tbsp capers and serve with your favourite potatoes. Follow with sliced bananas and fat-free natural yogurt.

greece is the word

breakfast

best-ever overnight oats ⓥ

**serves 1 / ready in 5 minutes,
plus overnight chilling**

Layer up 40g plain porridge oats
(Healthy Extra 'b'), fresh mango chunks,
raspberries, blueberries and fat-free
natural Greek yogurt in a glass. Cover,
chill overnight and stir well before
tucking in.

lunch

thai chicken lunchbox *SP*

serves 1 / ready in 10 minutes

Fill a lunchbox with salad leaves, sliced
skinless chicken breast, chopped cucumber,
red onion, coriander and red chilli. Mix 1 tbsp
each of Thai fish sauce (nam pla) and lime
juice with a pinch of sweetener and drizzle
over the salad.

dinner

greek lamb with lemon and garlic

serves 4 / ready in 1 hour 10 minutes, plus resting

Remove the visible fat from a 1.5kg leg of lamb, make lots of little slits and stuff them with fresh rosemary sprigs and sliced garlic. Season and put the lamb in a large roasting tin with a few rosemary sprigs, 2 garlic bulbs, halved horizontally, and 200ml boiling lamb stock. Squeeze over the juice of 1 lemon and roast at 220°C/fan 200°C/gas 7 for 15 minutes. Reduce the heat to 180°C/fan 160°C/gas 4 and cook for another 40 minutes. With 15 minutes to go, pour over the juice of another lemon and cover with lemon slices. Cover and rest for 10-15 minutes then garnish with rosemary sprigs, carve and serve with your favourite potatoes and Speed veg.

claw blimey

breakfast

rainbow BLT

serves 1 / ready in 10 minutes

Grill 2 back bacon rashers, visible fat removed, and pack between 2 slices of wholemeal toast from a small 400g loaf (Healthy Extra 'b') with lettuce, sliced yellow pepper and tomato. Follow with a ripe pear.

lunch

greek omelette Ⓥ ⓢⓟ

serves 1 / ready in 10 minutes

Beat a few eggs with a pinch of dried oregano and fry in low-calorie cooking spray. Top half of the omelette with baby spinach leaves and 65g diced reduced-fat feta (Healthy Extra 'a') then fold over the other half to cover. Serve with halved cherry tomatoes.

dinner

crab and courgetti linguine

serves 4 / ready in 15 minutes

Cook 400g dried linguine according to the pack instructions. Meanwhile, put
1 vegetable stock pot and 200ml water in a small saucepan and bring to the
boil over a medium heat. Add 2 crushed garlic cloves, 2 sliced spring onions,
1 finely chopped red chilli and the grated zest of ½ unwaxed lemon and boil for
2-3 minutes, adding 300g courgetti (or 2 large shredded courgettes) for the
final minute or so. Drain the pasta and stir into the sauce along with 2 drained
170g cans white crabmeat and some chopped fresh chives. Scatter over a little
more lemon zest, season to taste and serve with salad.

when life gives you lemons...

breakfast

passion fruit porridge Ⓥ Ⓢ𝐏

serves 1 / ready in 5 minutes

Make up 40g plain porridge oats (Healthy Extra 'b') with hot milk from your Healthy Extra 'a' allowance and stir in passion fruit pulp to serve.

lunch

salmon and potato salad

serves 1 / ready in 15 minutes

Boil some new potatoes, adding sugar snap peas for the last few minutes. Drain and stir through drained canned salmon, watercress and fat-free natural fromage frais. Season to taste. Follow with fresh blackberries.

dinner

lemon and chilli chicken with tuscan beans Ⓢ𝐏

serves 4 / ready in 30 minutes, plus marinating

Halve 4 skinless and boneless chicken breasts lengthways (to make 8 thin breasts) and put in a sealable food bag. Put the juice of 4 lemons and the zest of 1 into a bowl and add 2 tsp dried chilli flakes, 4 crushed garlic cloves and 1 tsp dried oregano. Season, whisk and pour into the bag. Seal, shake and chill for at least 2 hours. When you're nearly ready to eat, put 4 chopped shallots, 2 chopped garlic cloves, 200g halved cherry tomatoes and 100ml boiling chicken stock in a pan and cook for 8 minutes. Meanwhile, boil 400g halved green beans until tender in another pan and add to the tomatoes. Spray a griddle or frying pan with low-calorie cooking spray, place over a high heat and fry the chicken for 5 minutes each side or until cooked through, discarding the marinade. Scatter 2 tbsp chopped fresh parsley over the chicken and serve with the beans, lemon wedges and mashed celeriac.

steak that

breakfast

vedgeree

serves 1 / ready in 20 minutes

Briefly fry a few spring onions, 1 tsp mild curry powder and 70g dried basmati rice in a pan sprayed with low-calorie cooking spray. Add 150ml boiling water and bring to the boil, then cover and simmer for 12 minutes. Stand for 5 minutes, still covered, then fluff up the rice. Meanwhile, boil an egg or 2, peel and halve and serve on top. Follow with an orange.

lunch

steak sandwich

serves 1 / ready in 10 minutes

Fry sliced onion and your favourite lean beef steak, visible fat removed, in low-calorie cooking spray (2 minutes each side for rare, 3 for medium and 4 for well done). Make up a little mustard powder with water, stir in 1 tbsp fat-free natural fromage frais and spread on to 2 medium slices of wholemeal toast from a small 400g loaf (Healthy Extra 'b'). Rest the steak then slice and pile into the sandwich with lettuce, sliced tomato and the fried onion. Serve with gherkins. Follow with fat-free natural yogurt and sliced fresh kiwi fruit.

dinner

warm duck and grapefruit salad SP

serves 4 / ready in 35 minutes, plus marinating

In a shallow bowl, mix 4 tbsp light soy sauce,
2 star anise, 1 cinnamon stick, the juice of 3 limes
and 2cm piece root ginger, peeled and grated. Skin
4 duck breasts and trim off any visible fat, then add
to the marinade and turn to coat well. Marinate in the
fridge for 4 hours. Reserve the marinade and cook
the duck under a medium-high grill for 3-4 minutes
each side. Rest the duck for 10 minutes. Meanwhile,
bring the marinade to the boil in a small pan, simmer
for 6-8 minutes and pour into a bowl. In another
pan, boil 400g green beans for 2-3 minutes then
cool under cold water and mix with 2 segmented
grapefruits, 150g watercress, 8 sliced spring onions,
1 deseeded and chopped chilli and 1 shredded
cucumber. Divide the salad between plates. Slice the
duck, toss well in the cooked marinade and add to
the salad.

nice as pie

breakfast

smoked salmon and scrambled eggs

serves 1 / ready in 10 minutes

Fry lightly beaten eggs in a pan sprayed with low-calorie cooking spray, breaking up the eggs with a wooden spoon. Lift on to 2 medium slices of wholemeal toast from a small 400g loaf (Healthy Extra 'b') and top with smoked salmon and lemon juice. Follow with melon wedges.

lunch

sausage salad *SP*

serves 1 / ready in 20 minutes

Cook 2-3 Slimming World Syn-free Pork Sausages according to the pack instructions. Meanwhile, fill a shallow bowl with rocket, cherry tomatoes, cooked and cooled green beans and aubergine chunks fried in low-calorie cooking spray. Slice the sausages, add to the salad and drizzle with fat-free vinaigrette.

dinner

kale and mushroom pie ❄ *V* (vegan) (without the egg)

serves 4 / ready in 1 hour

Put 1 finely chopped leek, 1 large diced carrot, 400g sliced mushrooms (chestnut, button or portobello all work well), 400g chopped tomatoes and 1 vegetable stock pot in a saucepan and place over a high heat. Season to taste, bring to the boil and simmer for 15-20 minutes. Add 150g shredded kale and stir until wilted. Meanwhile, cut 800g peeled potatoes into chunks and boil until tender, then drain and mash. Pour the kale mixture into an ovenproof dish and cover evenly with the mash. Smooth with a fork, brush with beaten egg and bake at 200°C/fan 180°C/gas 6 for 25-30 minutes. Serve hot with extra Speed veg.

back of the net

breakfast

ham and egg cup *SP*

makes 1 / ready in 30 minutes

Lightly spray a ramekin with
low-calorie cooking spray and
line the base and sides with a slice
of lean ham, visible fat removed.
Fry up some mushrooms, spring
onions and tomato and tip into the
ramekin. Crack in an egg or 2 and
bake for 15-20 minutes at 180°C/
fan 160°C/gas 4. Follow with a peach.

lunch

courgette ribbon pasta *V*

serves 1 / ready in 15 minutes

Cook dried pasta shapes according
to the pack instructions and drain
well. Meanwhile, slice a courgette into
ribbons using a vegetable peeler and
fry over a medium-high heat for
5 minutes. Add a pinch of salt, a small
grated garlic clove and a little unwaxed
lemon zest and fry for 1 minute.
Remove from the heat, stir in 1 tbsp
fat-free natural fromage frais, chopped
fresh mint and a grind of black pepper
and stir it all into the pasta.

dinner

fresh trout salad

serves 4 / ready in 30 minutes

Poach 4 large trout fillets in boiling water for 10-12 minutes, then transfer to a plate and
cool slightly before skinning, removing any fine bones and flaking. Whisk 200g fat-free
natural yogurt, 1 crushed garlic clove, 1 tbsp white wine vinegar, 1 tsp mustard powder
and 3 tbsp chopped fresh dill and set aside. Roughly tear 1 romaine lettuce and place in
a wide salad bowl with 200g halved seedless grapes, 2 sliced celery sticks and 2 tbsp
chopped gherkins. Scatter over the trout and spoon over the yogurt dressing. Season and
scatter with extra dill to serve. Follow with fresh mango chunks and fat-free natural yogurt.

bowled over

breakfast

black forest brekkie (V)

serves 1 / ready in 5 minutes

Stir fresh berries into a Danone Activia 0% Fat Cherry yogurt. Scatter over 1 roughly chopped Double Choc Hi-fi bar (½ x Healthy Extra 'b').

lunch

cheesy chicken wraps

serves 1 / ready in 10 minutes

Toss chopped lettuce, tomato and red onion with sweetcorn, shredded cooked skinless chicken and lime juice to taste. Scatter over chopped coriander and 40g grated reduced-fat Cheddar (Healthy Extra 'a'). Spoon into Little Gem leaves to eat.

dinner

bibimbap (korean rice bowl) (V)

serves 4 / ready in 35 minutes

Cook 300g dried sushi rice (or short-grain rice) according to the pack instructions. Meanwhile, spray 2 frying pans with low-calorie cooking spray and place over a high heat. Cook 1 sliced red onion in 1 pan and 200g shiitake mushrooms in the other for 2-3 minutes then transfer to plates and keep warm. Spray the pans with more low-calorie cooking spray and cook 2 shredded carrots and 2 shredded courgettes in 1 pan, and 4 eggs to your liking in the other (see page 140). Divide the rice and veg between bowls and top with the eggs. Season to taste and serve with sliced chilli. Follow with a Hi-fi bar (½ x Healthy Extra 'b') and an apple.

push the boat out

breakfast

the full breakfast

serves 1 / ready in 25 minutes

Pile one half of a plate with cooked Slimming World Syn-free Pork Sausages, back bacon rashers, visible fat removed, and baked beans, and the other half with grilled mushrooms and tomatoes. Serve with a piping hot cuppa!

lunch

halloumi bap

 (if the halloumi is vegetarian)

serves 1 / ready in 15 minutes

Fry 35g sliced halloumi cheese (Healthy Extra 'a') and sliced courgette in low-calorie cooking spray. Pack into a 60g wholemeal roll (Healthy Extra 'b') and top with low-fat natural cottage cheese and a few oregano leaves. Follow with fresh plums.

dinner

lamb and couscous squash boats

serves 4 / ready in 1 hour

Halve and deseed 2 small butternut squashes, place cut-side up on a baking tray and roast at 200°C/fan 180°C/gas 6 for 45 minutes. Meanwhile, put 75g dried couscous in a heatproof bowl, pour in 125ml boiling water and cover with cling film. Put 1 chopped onion and a splash of water in a frying pan and cook over a medium heat for 5 minutes. Add 300g diced lean lamb leg steaks, visible fat removed, increase the heat to high and brown all over. Add 2 tsp cumin seeds, ½ tsp each ground cinnamon and chilli powder (heat to your taste), 2 tbsp tomato purée and the fluffed-up couscous and mix well. Scoop a cavity into each squash boat, chop the scooped bits and mix them into the lamb mixture. Divide the lamb mixture between the cavities and bake for 10 minutes. Sprinkle over 100g pomegranate seeds and serve with fat-free natural yogurt, lemon wedges and salad.

cook's tips

eggs

Pregnant women, the elderly, babies and toddlers are advised to choose eggs showing the British Lion stamp if eating raw or partially cooked eggs.

fat-free natural fromage frais, yogurt and plain quark

These are wonderful ingredients when you're Food Optimising as they give the creamy texture and taste normally achieved with cream. However, they tend to separate when boiled and can make the dish look unappetising. So unless the recipe says otherwise, add them off the heat once all the other ingredients have been cooked and simply heat through.

fresh, canned and frozen

Frozen ingredients and canned veg and beans are great alternatives to fresh foods and are so handy to have around. They'll keep for much longer, can be quicker to cook and are just as good for you. So feel free to switch between all three – bear in mind cooking times may change slightly.

fresh herbs

These lose their freshness quickly so if you have more than you can use, freeze them in a little water in ice cube trays – then you can add them straight to stews and curries.

fruit

While most fresh whole fruit is Free, puréed or cooked fruit counts as Syns because it isn't as filling and is much easier to over-consume.

low-calorie cooking spray

To cut down on fat in recipes, we recommend using non-stick cookware/ bakeware wherever possible. However, where you do need to use fat choose a low-calorie cooking spray which contains 1 calorie or less per spray, as these are Free – others would need to be counted as Syns. Ideal for fried eggs, roast potatoes and chips!

meat and poultry

Trim off any visible fat before cooking to make lean meat or poultry Free, and remember to remove the skin before or after cooking poultry. If you cook poultry with the skin on, cook it separately from the other ingredients so that the fat can't run into them (eg. don't roast potatoes in the same tin).

minced meat and poultry

Lean minced meat (5% fat or less) is a Free Food. Beef, pork and turkey mince are available in most major supermarkets at 5% fat or less – check the nutrition information to be sure. If possible, drain off any fat that comes from the mince while you're cooking it. Chicken and lamb mince isn't widely available with 5% fat or less so would have a Syn value… unless you fancy mincing it yourself (or you know a friendly butcher).

mustard powder

Made-up mustard in jars has Syns because it contains Synned ingredients while mustard powder is Free, making it a great choice for dressings and sauces.

seasoning

Where salt and pepper are used, we usually suggest seasoning to taste. Official advice is that adults should eat no more than 6g of salt a day.

stock

Fresh stock, stock cubes, stock pots, bouillon powder, ready-to-use liquid stock and liquid stock concentrate are all Free but be aware that gravy granules or powder and stock granules are not. Go for low-salt stock cubes to help cut your salt intake.

symbol sense

ready in…

This gives a guide to how long the recipe will take to prepare and cook.

serves…

This gives you an idea of how many people the recipe can serve. However, feel free to split the recipe between more or fewer people instead.

freezer-friendly ❄

Recipes showing this symbol can be safely frozen for up to 1 month. Keep in mind official advice on freezing safely:

- Label food for the freezer with details of what the meal is and when you cooked it.

- Make sure food has cooled before you put it in the freezer.

- Defrost frozen meals completely and reheat thoroughly before eating.

suitable for vegetarians

suitable for vegans vegan

Most bread and dried pasta is suitable for vegans but check the packaging to be sure.

Extra Easy

For super-charged weight loss, go for dishes marked Extra Easy SP. See your Food Optimising book for details or ask your Consultant.

Syns® selection

On top of all that Free Food and all those Healthy Extras, you can also enjoy your Syns. Most members stick within 5-15 Syns a day, and here we've featured some of the most popular options.

Biscuits & crispbreads, each unless stated

Bourbon creams	3.5
Breadsticks, plain, standard	1.0
Caxton Pink 'n' Whites	2.5
Cheese straws/twists	2.0
Chocolate chip cookies	3.0
Chocolate fingers	1.5
Cream crackers, standard	2.0
Crispbreads, original/rye	1.5
Custard creams	3.0
Digestive biscuit, chocolate-coated	4.0
Digestive biscuit, plain	3.5
Fig rolls	3.5
Fox's Party Ring biscuits	1.5
Ginger nuts/snaps	2.5
Jaffa cakes	2.5
Jam & mallow wheels eg. Wagon Wheels	5.0
Jam sandwich biscuits eg. Jammie Dodgers	4.5
Malted milk biscuits, plain	2.0
Nice biscuit	2.0
Oat biscuits, plain eg. Hobnobs	3.5
Oreo Sandwich Biscuits, Original	2.5
Rich tea biscuit, plain	2.0
Ritz Crackers, Original	1.0
Shortbread, fingers	4.5
Shortcake biscuits, fruit	2.0
Snack a Jacks Jumbo, Cheese/Salt & Vinegar	2.0
Tunnock's Milk/ Dark Chocolate Teacakes	5.0

Cakes, each unless stated

American-style mini muffin, choc chip/double chocolate	6.0
Cadbury Mini Roll, Milk Chocolate	6.0
Chocolate brownies, mini	3.0
Coconut macaroons	7.5
Doughnut ring, mini	3.0
Éclair, with cream & chocolate, mini	2.5
Fairy cakes, iced	5.0
Flapjack, plain, bitesize	4.0
Jam tart, individual	6.0
Meringue nest, plain	2.5
Mr Kipling French Fancies	5.5
Mr Kipling Mini Battenbergs	6.5
Viennese whirl	8.0

Chocolate

Bounty, single bar	7.0
Cadbury Buttons, 14.4g bag	4.0
Cadbury Curly Wurly, 26g bar	6.0
Celebrations, each	2.0
Heroes, each	2.5
Maltesers, 19.5g funsize bag	5.0
Mars Bar, 18g funsize bar	4.0
Milky Way, 15.5g funsize bar	3.5

Crisps & savoury snacks

Bombay mix, 25g	6.0
Cheese savouries, 25g	6.5
French Fries, all varieties, 18g bag	4.0
Hula Hoops, Original, 24g bag	6.0
Mini Cheddars, Original, 25g bag	6.5
Onion rings snacks, 25g	6.5
Pom-Bear, Original, 15g bag	4.0
Popcorn, popped with oil, salted/sweet, 25g	6.0
Pretzels, salted, 25g	5.0
Quavers, 16g bag	4.5
Skips, 13.1g bag	3.5
Twiglets, 24g bag	4.5
Walkers Crisps, 32.5g bag	8.5
Wotsits, 16.5g bag	4.5

Dressings & accompaniments, 1 level tbsp unless stated

Apple sauce, standard	0.5
Barbecue sauce	1.0

Brown sauce	1.0
Cranberry sauce	1.5
Dipping sauce, sweet chilli/hoisin	1.5
Gravy granules/paste, 1 level tsp	1.0
Mayonnaise, low-fat/extra-light	1.0
Mustard, English/Dijon/ Wholegrain, 1 level tsp	0.5
Oil, all varieties	6.0
Salad cream, reduced-fat/light	1.0
Sandwich pickle	1.0
Tartare sauce, standard	2.0
Tomato ketchup, standard	1.0
Tomato salsa	0.5

Drinks, alcoholic

Beer, standard, 3.5-4.1% vol, ½ pint	4.5
Cider, apple, ½ pint	6.0
Lager, reduced alcohol/ alcohol-free, 330ml bottle	3.5
Lager, standard, 4-6% vol, ½ pint	6.0
Red wine, medium alcohol (12.5-13.5% vol), 175ml	8.0
Rosé wine, medium alcohol (10.5-12.5% vol), 175ml	7.0
Sparkling wine e.g. Cava, Champagne, Prosecco (11-12% vol), 125ml	5.0
Spirits, 40% vol, 25ml	3.0

White wine, medium alcohol (10.5-12.5% vol), 175ml	7.0
Wine, reduced alcohol (5.5% vol), 175ml	4.0

Drinks, soft

Apple/Orange juice, unsweetened, 100ml	2.0
Cranberry/Mango juice drink, 100ml	2.5
Fanta, Orange, 330ml can	5.0
Cola, 250ml	5.5
Lemonade, 250ml	5.5
Shloer, Red/ White Grape, 250ml	5.5
Options Belgian Choc, 11g sachet	2.0

Fruit

Avocado, fresh, each	14.0
Dates, fresh, each	1.5
Olives, in brine, 8 olives	1.5
Olives, marinated, 8 olives	2.5

Ices, each unless stated

Nestlé Fab ice lolly, standard	4.0
Nestlé Fruit Pastilles ice lolly	2.5
Walls Calippo, Orange, standard	5.0
Walls Magnum, Classic, mini	8.5
Walls Mini Milk, all varieties	1.5
Walls Solero, Exotic	5.0
Walls Twister, standard	4.0

Nuts & seeds

Brazil nuts, plain, 25g	8.5
Cashew nuts, plain, 25g	7.5
Peanuts, plain, 25g	7.5
Pistachio nuts, shelled, 25g	7.5
Pumpkin seeds, 25g	7.5
Sunflower seeds, 25g	7.5

Spreads & sweet sauces, 1 level tsp unless stated

Aerosol cream, reduced-fat/ light, 3 level tbsp	0.5
Chocolate spread	1.5
Curd, lemon/lime/orange	1.0
Custard, canned/carton, low-fat, per 100g	4.5
Fat spread, extra-light/low-fat	0.5
Honey	1.0
Jam, standard	0.5
Maple syrup	0.5
Marmalade, standard	0.5
Peanut butter, standard	1.5

Sweets

Candyland Flumps, 12g each	2.0
Chew sweets eg. Starburst, each	1.0
Fruit pastilles/jellies, each	1.0
Jelly babies, each	1.0
Polo Mints, Sugar Free, 34g tube	4.0
Skittles, 18g bag	3.5

For the most up-to-date and accurate Syn values, from a database which contains thousands of products, call the Syns hotline on 09068 518 518* (UK only). Please have the packaging of the product you're querying on hand when you call so we can check it corresponds with that on our database.
*Calls are charged at 65p per minute, plus your telephone company's network access charge.

Syns selection